欢乐的游乐园

【美】丽莎·哈卡德尔◎著

【美】MH.皮尔兹◎绘

范晓星◎译

天津出版传媒集团

新蕾出版社

献给朱利安、琼安和美国凯恩出版社整个团队。感谢你们让我的创作充满乐趣!

——丽莎·哈卡德尔

献给大卫。

——MH.皮尔兹

图书在版编目 (CIP) 数据

欢乐的游乐园/(美)哈卡德尔(Harkrader,L.)著;
(美)皮尔兹(Pilz,MH.)绘;范晓星译.——天津:新
蕾出版社,2016.7(2024.12 重印)
(数学帮帮忙·互动版)
书名原文:Ruby Makes It Even
ISBN 978-7-5307-6400-8

Ⅰ.①欢… Ⅱ.①哈…②皮…③范… Ⅲ.①数学–
儿童读物Ⅳ.①01–49

中国版本图书馆 CIP 数据核字(2016)第 078045 号

Ruby Makes It Even by Lisa Harkrader;
Illustrated by MH Pilz.
Text copyright © 2015 by Lisa Harkrader.
Illustrations copyright © 2015 by MH Pilz.
All rights reserved, including the right of reproduction in whole or in part in any form.
This edition published by arrangement with Kane Press, Inc. New York, NY, represented by The ChoiceMaker Korea Co.
Simplified Chinese translation copyright © 2016 by New Buds Publishing House (Tianjin) Limited Company
ALL RIGHTS RESERVED
本书中文简体版专有出版权经由中华版权代理中心授予新蕾出版社(天津)有限公司。未经许可,不得以任何方式复制或抄袭本书的任何部分。
津图登字:02–2015–225

出版发行:天津出版传媒集团
　　　　　　　新蕾出版社
http://www.newbuds.com.cn
地　　址:天津市和平区西康路 35 号(300051)
出 版 人:马玉秀
电　　话:总编办 (022)23332422
　　　　　　发行部 (022)23332679　23332351
传　　真:(022)23332422
经　　销:全国新华书店
印　　刷:天津新华印务有限公司
开　　本:787mm×1092mm　1/16
印　　张:3
版　　次:2016 年 7 月第 1 版　2024 年 12 月第 20 次印刷
定　　价:12.00 元

无处不在的数学

资深编辑　卢　江

　　人们常说"兴趣是最好的老师",有了兴趣,学习就会变得轻松愉快。数学对于孩子来说或许有些难,因为比起语文,数学显得枯燥、抽象,不容易理解,孩子往往不那么喜欢。可许多家长都知道,学数学对于孩子的成长和今后的生活有多么重要。不仅数学知识很有用,学习数学过程中获得的数学思想和方法更会影响孩子的一生,因为数学素养是构成人基本素质的一个重要因素。但是,怎样才能让孩子对数学产生兴趣呢?怎样才能激发他们兴致勃勃地去探索数学问题呢?我认为,让孩子读些有趣的书或许是不错的选择。读了这套"数学帮帮忙",我立刻产生了想把它们推荐给教师和家长朋友们的愿望,因为这真是一套会让孩子爱上数学的好书!

　　这套有趣的图书从美国引进,原出版者是美国资深教育专家。每本书讲述一个孩子们生活中的故事,由故事中出现的问题自然地引入一个数学知识,然后通过运用数学知识解决问题。比如,从帮助外婆整理散落的纽扣引出分类,从为小狗记录藏骨头的地点引出空间方位等等。故事素材全部来源于孩子们的真实生活，不是童话，不是幻想，而是鲜活的生活实例。正是这些发生在孩子身边的故事，让孩子们懂得，数学无处不在并且非常有用；这些鲜活的实例也使得抽象的概念更易于理解，更容易激发孩子学习数学的兴趣，让他们逐渐爱上数学。这样的教育思想和方法与我国近年来提倡的数学教育理念是十分吻合的！

这是一套适合5~8岁孩子阅读的书，书中的有趣情节和生动的插画可以将抽象的数学问题直观化、形象化，为孩子的思维活动提供具体形象的支持。如果亲子共读的话，家长可以带领孩子推测情节的发展，探讨解决难题的办法，让孩子在愉悦的氛围中学到知识和方法。

值得教师和家长朋友们注意的是，在每本书的后面，出版者还加入了"互动课堂"及"互动练习"，一方面通过一些精心设计的活动让孩子巩固新学到的数学知识，进一步体会知识的含义和实际应用；另一方面帮助家长指导孩子阅读，体会故事中数学之外的道理，逐步提升孩子的阅读理解能力。

我相信孩子读过这套书后一定会明白，原来，数学不是烦恼，不是包袱，数学真能帮大忙！

雨林游乐园

"露比！"米莉攥紧我的胳膊，"我们到了。"

"终于到了！"贝丝说。

我们期待学校组织游园活动，都盼了一整年了。现在，我们终于如愿以偿。

"雨林游乐园。"我喃喃地说。

一阵轰鸣声过后，我们的校车终于停了下来。米莉、贝丝、我，还有我们蓝顿小学的其他同学争先恐后地下了车。

老师把我们分成几组。

哎呀，不好！我的弟弟莱瑞摇摇晃晃地朝我跑来。他举着胳膊假装是大象鼻子。"露比，你看！"他说，"我是大象！"

这还不算，我那个什么都要说了算的姐姐乔乔也大步朝我走来。"露比，你要当心……"

　　"我知道啦！"没等她说完，我就一溜烟跑走了。我不要乔乔管我，也不要莱瑞令人尴尬的玩笑，我就是不要他俩毁掉我美好的一天。

　　我躲开了他们，一直跟着我最好的两个朋友——米莉和贝丝。

我们三人兴冲冲地走进游乐园。

我们停下脚步抬头看着高空中的游乐项目。这些游乐项目我们听人说过，在广告上也看到过。现在，它们就在我们眼前，高耸入云。

"梦谷激流。"贝丝小声说。

我们正看着的时候，一只木筏载满游客，从梦谷山顶呼啸而落。木筏在激流中飞速漂流，在漩涡中旋转，最终消失在伸手不见五指的山洞中。

接下来是惊心动魄的时刻，只听山洞里的尖叫声起伏回荡。我都不敢喘气了。

木筏从山洞的另一侧一跃而出，它好像在半空中悬了片刻，然后随着梦谷瀑布一落而下，一头扎进下面的湖水里，溅起无数的水花。

真好玩儿呀！太刺激啦！

我们惊讶得合不拢嘴。

看起来好吓人！

"我们去吧。"米莉拔腿朝梦谷激流走去。

"不！"我忍不住大叫一声，"我是说，雨林特快就在这儿。我们先坐这个吧。"

米莉停下脚步说："我们盼着坐这个梦谷激流，盼了一整年哪！"

米莉的话没错，可那是在我真的见到它之前。

　　"我们投票表决。"我提议,"谁想去坐雨林特快?"

　　我立刻举起手。米莉把胳膊抱在胸前。我俩都看着贝丝。

　　贝丝慢慢地举起手说:"把最好玩儿的梦谷激流留在最后吧。"

　　好消息:还有一整天呢,我可以慢慢地积攒勇气。

　　坏消息:一整天我可都要为这事心里打鼓了。

我们坐上雨林特快。

贝丝找到一个前面的座位。米莉一屁股坐在她旁边。她俩挤着坐，可我还是坐不下。

我爬到她们身后的座位。我对自己说："一个人坐也挺好。"

但其实孤零零的感觉一点儿都不好。

3是奇数。

坐过雨林特快之后，我们又投票表决去坐蟒蛇出洞。这次我坐在了贝丝旁边。米莉坐在我们身后，这次轮到她孤零零一个人了。看到好朋友被撇在一边我心里也不好受。

好消息：我们就这样一直用投票的方式来决定去坐哪个游乐项目。

棉花糖

坏消息：大多数游乐项目是两人座。我们轮流配对，可总有一个人必须孤零零的。

还有，不论我们去坐哪个游乐项目，都能看到梦谷激流。

我们又要投票表决的时候，我看到了弟弟莱瑞和他的朋友卡洛斯与亚麦尔。他们怀抱着好多零食，像鳄鱼一样张着嘴巴吃呀，吃呀。

趁莱瑞还没发现我，我拉起米莉和贝丝往
树屋探险跑。

　　我们一下撞上了鲍勃，他是我阅读小组里的同学。

　　"你的小组呢？"米莉问。

　　鲍勃耸耸肩膀说："我们组有三个人，可座位都是双人的。我正好落单。"

　　"现在你是一个人。"贝丝说，"你真成了多余的小孩儿。"

　　突然，我有了一个绝佳的主意。

"你是奇数,一个人。"我对鲍勃说,"我们也是奇数,三个人。奇数加奇数的和是偶数。"

鲍勃马上眉开眼笑了。"4是偶数,这么说就不会有人落单了。"

4是偶数。

我们四人组出发了。我们去坐了丛林越野、青藤秋千和冲天鹦鹉。这几个游乐项目的座位都是四人一排，没有人单独坐一边。

　　梦谷激流的阴影还是笼罩在我心里，不过我玩得太开心了，倒不觉得那么害怕了。

实际上,我心里有点儿小小的期待了。

这么一想,我都等不及了。

都是因为偶数哇!

"问题解决了。"我说,"偶数就是比奇数好!"

"下面我们该坐哪个了？"鲍勃问。

"我选鳄鱼独木舟。"贝丝说。

"我也选这个。"我说。

"我选亚马孙迷宫。"米莉说。

鲍勃点点头说："那边排队的人很少。"

我们四个你看看我，我瞧瞧你。偶数是很好，可遇到平局就没招儿了。

　　我们正想法子要怎么解决的时候，弟弟莱瑞和他的伙伴们一步一晃地走了过来。他们的脸色铁青。

　　"我们到处找你。"莱瑞哼哼唧唧地说。

　　"我们难受死了。"卡洛斯说。

　　"我们吃撑着了。"亚麦尔说。

莱瑞真是个讨厌的家伙，老是开一些莫名其妙的玩笑。

　　可他毕竟是我的亲弟弟呀。

　　"我得照顾他。"我说。

　　米莉、贝丝和鲍勃都表示同意。他们举手表决，通过了莱瑞和他的朋友们也加入我们的提议。

好消息：偶数加奇数是奇数。现在我们有七个人了，不会有平局的烦恼了。

坏消息：莱瑞、卡洛斯和亚麦尔都有气无力的，玩什么都不开心。我们只能去坐懒骨头海獭了，它就是只小木船，在梦谷激流下面的湖里漂来漂去。

玩过这个项目，我帮着莱瑞和他的朋友们下了木船。

7 是奇数。

　　这时，我们又遇到了姐姐乔乔。她和她的朋友卡莱
尔和希斯在一起。

　　"老师说上校车之前还有时间再玩一个项目。"乔
乔告诉我们。

　　"梦谷激流！"米莉、鲍勃和贝丝大喊。

　　莱瑞、卡洛斯和亚麦尔痛苦地呻吟着。

　　我叹了一口气说："你们去吧，别管我了。我把这几
个讨厌鬼送到校车那边去。"

乔乔眉头一皱说："让你的朋友们撇下你去玩这个游戏吗？你错过了整个游乐园最好玩儿的项目！"她又板起脸瞪着莱瑞说："我知道你不舒服，可你现在就得好起来。别给我们拖后腿，我们要去玩梦谷激流。"

　　我眨眨眼睛问："我们？"

　　"是呀,我们一起。"乔乔说。"卡莱尔、希斯和我把梦谷激流留到最后坐呢。你们要是不能去,我也不去了。你是我的妹妹。我要照顾你。"

　　于是,乔乔和她的朋友们也加入了我们的小组。她们是奇数,我们是奇数,现在又成偶数了。

只要莱瑞和他的伙伴们爬到梦谷山顶就行了。或许是乔乔严厉的眼神起了作用吧。不管怎么说，当我们到山顶的时候，他们三个人的脸色也不那么难看了。

我们全坐进了木筏。座位正好是个偶数——10。这也正是我们这组的人数。

10 是偶数。

梦谷激流
入口

27

我们系好安全带，木筏"嗖"地冲入湖中。我们在激流中飞速漂流，在漩涡中旋转，最终消失在伸手不见五指的山洞中。

　　我们大声尖叫起来。

然后,我们从山洞的另一侧一跃而出,木筏好像在半空中停了片刻,接着又随梦谷瀑布一落而下,一头扎进下面的湖水里。

好消息：真好玩儿呀！ 太刺激了！

更好的消息：真的很吓人。不过这样更好玩儿了。

最好的消息：没有一个人是单独坐的。

奇数、偶数表

偶数（能被 2 整除的数）	奇数（不能被 2 整除的数）
0	1
2	3
4	5
6	7
8	9

偶数的个位是：2、4、6、8、0

奇数的个位是：1、3、5、7、9

小测试：数字 10 是偶数还是奇数？

（提示，看数字的最后一位。）

亲爱的家长朋友，请您和孩子一起完成下面这些内容，会有更大的收获哟！

提高阅读能力

• 请看书的封面，大声读出书名。让孩子猜猜这会是一个怎样的故事？让孩子根据以往的经验，回想一下游乐园里游乐项目的座位是单人座还是双人座。和孩子一起重新读一遍故事，重点看第 11 页、第 17 页、第 23 页和第 27 页，小方框里的信息可以帮助孩子理解奇数和偶数的概念。

• 露比和朋友们玩一开始的两个游乐项目时遇到了问题。请看第 17 页，她们最后是如何解决的呢？

互动课堂

巩固数学概念

- 和孩子一起在纸上画一画，帮助孩子理解奇数、偶数的概念，例如，////=4；///////=7。

- 由于偶数可以被 2 整除，所以除 0 外的偶数，都可以在纸上将其分解成相同的 2 组。例如，4 分解成 2 个 2（// //）；8 分解成 2 个 4（////　////）。那么奇数可以分解成相同的 2 组吗？在纸上画一画吧。

- 请看第 20 页，当需要投票表决的时候，人数是偶数会有什么问题？露比和朋友们是怎么解决的？

生活中的数学

- 提醒孩子刚才是如何用斜线来分辨出某个数是奇数还是偶数的。在纸上写下数字 2、5、6、8、9。这几个数字是奇数还是偶数？画一画来找出答案吧！

- 想一想，跟朋友做游戏时，人数是偶数的时候在哪些方面有利，又在哪些方面有弊？

互动练习！

桌子上摆了以下几种水果，你能说出各种水果的总数分别是奇数还是偶数吗？

请根据数的排列顺序，将表格填充完整，然后回答如下几个问题：

1	2	3		5	6	7	8		10
	12	13	14		16	17	18	19	

①上述表格中，哪些是奇数？

②上述表格中，哪些是偶数？

③上述表格中，比 8 小的偶数有哪些？

④上述表格中，比 16 大的奇数有哪些？

露比、米莉和贝丝在看校园里同学们做游戏。A 组有 5 人在跳绳,B 组有 2 人在踢毽子,C 组有 6 人在玩老鹰捉小鸡。你能帮他们回答下列问题吗?

现在跳绳的有 5 人,我去参加后,跳绳的人数是奇数还是偶数?

踢毽子好玩儿,我去参加后,踢毽子的人数变成奇数还是偶数?

玩老鹰捉小鸡的人数是偶数,我带几个人去参加,能保证玩的人数还是偶数呢?

将 30 块糖果分给米莉和贝丝。

①如果米莉得到的糖果数是奇数，那么贝丝得到的糖果数是奇数还是偶数？

②如果米莉得到的糖果数是偶数，那么贝丝得到的糖果数是奇数还是偶数？

通过故事的学习,我们知道,可以被 2 整除的数是偶数,不能被 2 整除的数是奇数。根据这个知识点,你能回答下列问题吗?

①篮子里有一些苹果,2 个 2 个地数,数了 5 次正好数完,那么篮子里一共有多少个苹果?苹果的总数是奇数还是偶数?

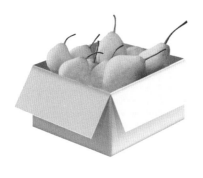

②箱子里有一些梨,2 个 2 个地拿,拿了 4 次,还剩 1 个,那么箱子里一共有多少个梨?梨的总数是奇数还是偶数?

③把 9 支铅笔,分给 3 个小朋友,不要求每个人分得的铅笔数一样多,但要求每个人得到的铅笔数必须是双数,这可以做到吗?

39

互动练习6

你可以不通过计算，就将各个算式的结果填入相应的圆圈内吗？

①12+3
②28+10
③34+11
④7+9
⑤16+22
⑥26+11

结果是偶数：

结果是奇数：

露比出去玩住酒店，被安排在了酒店 2 层。左手边的房间号都是单数，右手边的房间号都是双数。乔乔住在右手边的第 4 个房间，右手边的第一个房间号是 202，那么你知道乔乔的房间号是多少吗？

互动练习1:

香蕉和西瓜各自的总数是偶数。

苹果和梨各自的总数是奇数。

互动练习2:

1	2	3	4	5	6	7	8	9	10
11	12	13	14	15	16	17	18	19	20

①奇数:1、3、5、7、9、11、13、15、17、
　　19

②偶数:2、4、6、8、10、12、14、16、
　　18、20

③2、4、6

④17、19

互动练习3:

露比参加跳绳后人数是6,是偶
数。

贝丝参加踢毽子后人数是3,是
奇数。

答案不唯一,只要米莉带的人数
为奇数即可。

互动练习4:

①奇数

②偶数

互动练习5:

①10 个;偶数

②9 个;奇数

③不可以

互动练习6:

结果是偶数的:②④⑤

结果是奇数的:①③⑥

互动练习7:

208

(习题设计:何　晨)

Ruby Makes It Even

"Ruby!" Millie squeezes my arm. "We're here."

"At last!" says Beth.

We've been waiting all year for our school trip. Now we realized our dream.

"Rainforest Fun Park," I whisper.

Our bus rumbles to a stop. Millie, Beth, and I pile out—along with everyone else from Langston Elementary.

The teachers begin sorting us into groups.

Oh, no. My little brother, Leroy, lumbers toward me, swinging his arms like a trunk. "Ruby, look!" he says. "I'm an elephant."

Even worse, my bossy older sister, Jo, strides over. "Ruby, be sure you—"

"I know." I scurry off before she can finish. I don't need Jo's bossiness—or Leroy's annoying jokes—wrecking my day.

I dodge them both and stick with my two best friends, Millie and Beth.

The three of us troop into the park.

We stop and stare up. And up. We've heard about it. We've seen ads. Now here it is, towering above us.

"Mongo Scream," whispers Beth.

As we watch, a raft loaded with riders swoops into the river at the top of Mongo Mountain. It hurtles over rapids, spins around whirlpools, and vanishes into a dark cavern.

For a few tense moments, shrieks and squeals echo from inside. I hold my breath.

The raft shoots out the other side. It hangs in the air, then plummets down Mongo Waterfall and splashes into the lake below.

It looks fun! It looks thrilling!

We gulp.

It looks scary.

"Let's go." Millie sets off for Mongo Scream.

"No!" I cry, before I can stop myself. "I mean, Locomotive Jungle is right here. Let's ride it first."

Millie stops. "We've been waiting to ride Mongo Scream all year."

That was before I'd actually seen it.

"Let's vote," I say. "Who wants to ride Locomotive Jungle?"

I quickly raise my hand. Millie crosses her arms over her chest. We turn to Beth.

Slowly she raises her hand."Let's save the best—Mongo Scream—for last."

Good news: I have the whole day to work up my courage.

Bad news: I have the whole day to worry about Mongo Scream.

We scramble aboard Locomotive Jungle.

Beth finds a bench up front. Millie slides in beside her. They try to scoot closer, but there isn't any more room.

I crawl onto the bench behind them. I tell myself it's great to have a seat to myself.

But it's no fun being odd kid out.

Three is an odd number.

After Locomotive Jungle, we vote to ride the Python. This time I sit beside Beth. Millie sits behind us—by herself. It's no fun seeing your friends left out, either.

Good news: We keep voting and riding.

Bad news: All the rides are made for even numbers. We take turns pairing up, but someone always has to ride alone.

Plus everywhere we go, Mongo Scream looms overhead.

We're about to vote again when I spot Leroy with his friends Carlos and Jamal. They're carrying armloads of snacks and snapping their jaws like crocodiles.

Before Leroy can see me, I pull Millie and Beth into the Treehouse Arcade and run smack into Rob, a kid from my reading group.

"Where's your group?" Millie asks him.

Rob shrugs. "Our group had three. But the rides are for even numbers.

I was odd kid out."

"But now you're by yourself," says Beth. "You're really odd kid out."

Suddenly I've got a brilliant idea.

"You're an odd number—one," I tell Rob. "We're an odd number—three. But an odd plus an odd makes an even."

Rob's eyes grow wide. "And an even four means nobody's left out."

Four is an even number.

The four of us set off. We ride Jungle Jalopies, Swinging Vine, and Parrot Plunge. The seats are four across, so nobody has to ride alone.

Mongo Scream still looms overhead, but I'm having such a great time that it doesn't seem as scary.

In fact, I'm looking forward to it.

Come to think of it, I can hardly wait.

All because of an even number.

"That settles it," I say. "Evens are way better than odds."

"What should we ride next?" says Rob.

"I vote Crocodile Canoes," says Beth.

"Me too," I say.

"I vote Amazon Zing," says Millie.

Rob nods. "It has a shorter line."

We look at each other. An even number is great—until you can't break a tie.

We're trying to decide what to do when Leroy and his friends trudge up. They look a little green.

"We've been searching for you everywhere," moans Leroy.

"We don't feel so good," says Carlos.

"We ate a lot of snacks," says Jamal.

Leroy can be annoying. Leroy makes awful jokes.

But Leroy's my little brother.

"I have to take care of him," I say.

Millie, Beth, and Rob agree. They vote for Leroy and his friends to join our group.

Good news: An even plus an odd makes an odd. Now we have seven. We can break our tie.

Bad news: Leroy, Carlos, and Jamal are too sick to ride anything fun. We end up on the Lazy Sloth, a boat that drifts around the lake below Mongo Scream.

When the ride ends, I help Leroy and his friends off and run straight into Jo. She's with her friends Claire and Heather.

Seven is an odd number.

"Our teachers said we have time for one more ride before we load the buses," Jo tells us.

"Mongo Scream!" shout Millie, Rob, and Beth.

Leroy, Carlos, and Jamal moan.

I sigh. "Go on without me. I'll get these guys to the bus."

Jo frowns. "And let your friends ride without you? You'll miss the best ride in the park! " Jo gives Leroy a stern look. "I know you feel sick," she says, "but you need to start feeling better. You don't want to keep us off Mongo Scream."

I blink. "Us?"

"Yes, us," says Jo. "Claire, Heather, and I saved Mongo Scream for last. I won't go if you're stuck here. You're my little sister. I have to look out for you."

So Jo and her friends join our group. They're an odd, and we're an odd, so we're even again.

The hike up Mongo Mountain is just what Leroy and his friends need. Or maybe Jo's stern look does the trick. Either way, they're less green by the time we reach the top.

We scramble aboard our raft. It seats an even number: ten. Which happens to be exactly the same number as our group.

Ten is an even number.

We strap in, and the raft swoops into the river. We hurtle over rapids, spin around whirlpools, and plunge into a dark cavern.

We shriek and squeal.

Then we shoot out the other side. The raft hangs in the air for a moment before we plummet down the Mongo Waterfall and splash into the pool below.

Good news: It's fun! It's thrilling!

Better news: It's scary. But that just makes it more fun.

Best news: Nobody has to be odd kid out.